John Thompson's Modern Course for the Piano

The SECOND GRADE BOOK

Something New Every Lesson

Stories and Biographical Sketches by
Laurence B. Ellert

Drawings by
Doris *and* George Hauman

**FOLLOWS UNINTERRUPTEDLY AND
IN PROGRESSIVE SEQUENCE THE
MUSICAL FOUNDATION DEVELOPED
BY THE "FIRST GRADE BOOK"**

CHAPPELL & CO. LTD.

THE WILLIS MUSIC COMPANY. CINCINNATI, OHIO
PRINTED IN ENGLAND

PREFACE

SINCE the plan of the author's Modern Course for the Piano is to make the teachers' and pupils' work so pleasing that it will lead to the quickest and best results, THIS BOOK TAKES UP EXACTLY WHERE "THE FIRST GRADE BOOK" LEFT OFF. Briefly, it continues, uninterruptedly, to "make haste slowly", but surely and steadily.

With consideration for the needs of MODERN BEGINNERS, the contents of this, *The Second Grade Book*, are not limited strictly to piano music. In order that the young student may experience the joy of a COURSE IN APPRECIATION as well as of PIANISM, examples (with explanatory notes) from Light Opera, Ballet, Grand Opera, Oratorio, Songs, etc. have been included. Hence, the slogan "Something New Every Lesson" follows in logical sequence.

TECHNICAL AND MUSICAL PROGRESSION

In THE FIRST GRADE BOOK most of the examples remained necessarily in the *five-finger position*. In this book, the positions become gradually more extended. The thumbs are trained to pass under and the hands over; Leger lines are introduced; the Pedals explained; Major Scales and their Minors, both Relative and Parallel, are presented; Examples in Hand Expansion, Cadence Chords, Arpeggios, the Dominant-Seventh Chord, as well as, Lessons in Chord Analysis, Trill Studies and, of course, the Various Touches are included.

Most of the pieces are preceded by short technical exercises, which in many cases, are subtle illustrations on *how to practise*—an art in itself.

MAKING MUSICIANS

Everything possible has been done to encourage the pupil to *think and feel musically;* to play with musical understanding so that his progress will be measured by increased enjoyment, as well as in terms of technical proficiency.

Examples from the Masters include Bach, Handel, Haydn, Mozart, Beethoven, Chopin, Liszt, Auber, Ponchielli, Bizet, and Offenbach. It is the sincere wish of the author that pupils who complete this book will have become not only better pianists but also *better musicians* and that the urge to explore still deeper into the wonderful realm of music will have been intelligently stimulated.

John Thompson

P.S. *Certificate of Merit (Diploma) will be found on page 91.*

CONTENTS

"Something New Every Lesson"

Hand in NORMAL
five-finger position

Hand position with thumb
UNDER the second finger

Before playing this piece place your hand as in figure 1 and practise the following exercise with the RIGHT HAND until the thumb can be passed under smoothly without turning the hand. The hand (or rather the arm) must pivot over on the thumb without breaking at the wrist.

In the Alps

Andantino

NOTE: The importance of the preparatory exercise cannot be overestimated. Smooth passage playing cannot be developed until the pivoting motion of the hand over the thumb has been mastered. These exercises should therefore be carried in review until they can be done with ease. For technical drills see page 89.

W. M. Co. 5770
(42980)

LIGHT OPERA or MUSICAL COMEDY is a play set to music in which part of the dialogue is sung and part of it spoken. Such works usually have a happy ending. "Fra Diavolo" (Brother Devil) which derives its name from the hero, a famous Italian bandit, is a comic opera in 3 acts; music by the French composer, Daniel Francois Esprit Auber. It was first given in Paris in 1830.

Fra Diavolo as the Marquis—Act I

Zerlina, an innkeeper's daughter is betrothed to Lorenzo, a soldier, but they are too poor to marry. Fra Diavolo, disguised as the Marquis San Marco, is travelling with two English tourists, Lord and Lady Allcash, in order to rob them of money and jewels. When the party arrives at the inn and tells of an attempted robbery by highwaymen, Zerlina, believing Fra Diavolo to be a real marquis, tells him the story of this bold bandit's life in the aria (solo) "On Yonder Rock Reclining". That night, after the guests retire, the marquis (Fra Diavolo) with several of his followers, conceals himself in Zerlina's room to rob Lord Allcash. Lorenzo, who has been ordered to pursue the bandits, arrives with a party of soldiers and arrests two of the robbers while Fra Diavolo escapes to the mountains. In the third act, he is captured. Lorenzo receives a handsome reward, marries Zerlina, and they live happily ever afterwards.

Always
Be
Careful
to pass the thumb under smoothly

On Yonder Rock Reclining

D. F. E. Auber (1782-1821)

Hop O' My Thumb

Dynamics.

Moderato

For additional Exercises see page 89

W. M. Co. 5770

8

Morning Prayers in the Bach Family
(Painting by Rosenthal)
Courtesy Photographic Society, Berlin — N. Y. Graphic Society, N. Y.—Agents

Johann Sebastian Bach, the greatest of all the masters of music, came of a musical family whose ancestors for nearly 200 years had been noted among the townspeople of Eisenach, Germany. The story is told that his great-great-grandfather, a very jovial miller, used to sit in the door of his mill and sing and play his zither while the mill-wheel went 'round and 'round grinding the grain. At the age of ten, Johann's father died and he went to live with his brother, also a musician. As it was difficult to get music in those days, young Bach used to copy his brother's music by the moonlight. At the age of eighteen, he often walked for miles, sometimes without food, en route to Hamburg where he could listen to concerts. Toward the end of his life, Bach was a great favourite among the princes and kings. Nothing gave him as much pleasure as having his many children and relations assemble in the Bach home and play music.

Menuet

Moderato

J. S. Bach (1685-1750)

The Menuet is a very old dance of French origin. Its title is derived from the French word *menu* (small) and refers to the steps of the dance. It should be played at a rather deliberate tempo and as gracefully as possible. Be sure to observe all phrasing marks.

LEGER-LINES are short lines used on notes which lie ABOVE or BELOW the staff.

LEGER-SPACES are the spaces between the leger lines ABOVE or BELOW the staff.

LEGER-LINES or SPACES are counted either UP or DOWN,
away from the staff and are very easy to recognize if
we remember them as BORROWED LINES or SPACES.

Leger-lines and Spaces ABOVE the Treble Staff

If we imagine five lines drawn above the TOP line of the treble staff and mark the leger-lines, the FIRST BORROWED LINE will give us the position of A and B. TWO BORROWED LINES will show the position of C and D *etc.*

The following illustration shows how All leger-lines and spaces in the Bass clef (above Middle C) are lines and spaces Borrowed from the Treble clef.

These notes in the Treble clef when transposed to Bass clef appear as above in music.

Note that the LINES indicat-
ed by the dotted extension of
the staff show what LINES and
SPACES were BORROWED from
the TREBLE CLEF.

To read or write notes Below middle C in the Treble clef we Borrow leger-lines and spaces from the Bass clef.

These notes in the Bass clef when transposed to Treble clef appear as above in music

Please notice that the notes shown
on the dotted extension of the staff
occupy the same LINES and SPACES
BORROWED from BASS CLEF.

W. M. Co. 5770

CHROMATIC PROGRESSIONS

This piece is built on chromatic progressions. Learn to play the RIGHT HAND MELODY PATTERN first. Notice that it is repeated in several positions.

RIGHT HAND MELODY PATTERN

Next, practise the following LEFT HAND PREPARATORY EXERCISE.

LEFT HAND

'Round the Village

Con moto

G. + D. HAUMAN

THE SIGNATURE FOR COMMON TIME
and its origin

○ A CIRCLE, the most perfect geometrical figure, was used in medieval music to indicate perfect time, *tempus perfectum.*

C THE BROKEN CIRCLE, an imperfect figure, was used to designate imperfect time *tempus imperfectum.*

C The modern version of the broken circle, suggesting the letter C, is placed in the Time Signature to indicate $\frac{4}{4}$

Practise this PREPARATORY EXERCISE before playing *"Country Gardens".*
Play the three-note groups with finger legato, tossing off each group at the end of the slur sign. There are three sets of fingers given. Each set should be studied. Practise first each hand separately, then together, an octave apart.

Country Gardens
Old English Morris Dance

From the Morris Dance Tunes, Set 1.   By permission of Novello and Company, Limited.

W. M. Co. 5770

10

BALLET is a pantomime telling a story in dance and music. The ballet is often introduced in an opera or stage piece aided by spectacular scenery and costumes. It is not necessarily part of an opera but may be complete in itself. "Dance of the Hours" is a classic ballet which was written for the opera "La Gioconda" by Amilcare Ponchielli, an Italian composer, who was the teacher of Puccini. The opera was first performed in Milan, April, 1876.

Radio City Music Hall Corps de Ballet

The scene is laid in Venice in the 17th century. La Gioconda, a beautiful street singer, is loved by Barnaba, a spy; but she spurns him because she is in love with Enzo, a Genoese nobleman. In revenge, Barnaba incites the people against Gioconda's blind mother, accusing her of witchcraft. The mother is saved by Enzo who, having incurred the displeasure of the "council," is obliged to disguise himself as a fisherman. In Act 3, the great hall of the Ducal Palace is filled with masqueraders for the ball. The Duke announces the ballet in which the dancers, costumed as the Hours of Dawn, Day, Evening, and Night, portray the struggle between day and night. In the finale, the hours of light conquer the hours of darkness.

PHRASING: Ability to phrase gracefully is absolutely necessary to good piano playing. It not only adds style to your playing but also gives life and animation to the music.

Preparatory Exercise

Dance of the Hours

Moderato

Ponchielli (1834-1886)

p lightly and gracefully

Prelude

Christmas Carol

SOME of the carols sung at Christmas time are older than folk-music. The word "carol", in the early centuries, meant *circle-dance;* a form in which the dancers sang to their own accompaniment. Carol dances were used for various festival seasons, New Year's Day, Easter, Christmas, etc. In medieval times, dances used by the nobility were called *Carolles*. This beautiful Christmas Carol from Hungary should be played joyously. Try to make it suggest sleigh bells and in the gay spirit typical of the Yuletide. Play the left hand with *wrist staccato* and in the right hand be sure to make a distinction between the sustained chords and the staccato chords (wrist).

"Una corda" or Soft pedal - - - - - - - - - → ← - - - - - - - Damper pedal

Sostenuto pedal

THE modern Grand Piano is equipped with three pedals. The pedal on the right is called the DAMPER PEDAL because when pressed down it raises up all dampers off the strings, thereby permitting all strings which have been struck to continue vibrating. In other words, *prolonging the SOUND of strings affected.*

The pedal on the left is known as the SOFT PEDAL. It gives a softer and lighter tone. (Although it functions differently on Uprights than on Grands). It is usually indicated in music by the words "una corda."

The Middle Pedal (on all Grands) is called the SOSTENUTO PEDAL. It sustains only such keys as are held down at the moment the pedal is applied. In many Upright Pianos the Middle Pedal is constructed so that it may be used as a PRACTICE PEDAL. When in use, a strip of felt is lowered between the hammers and the strings, thus deadening the sound and also the quality of tone.

For the present, we shall study the use of the DAMPER PEDAL only. In the early part of the pupil's career it will be used for sustaining purposes but later on, it will be studied and used for colour values as well.

There are many different signs to indicate when and where and how long to use the damper pedal but in this book the following sign will be employed throughout.

Press down here

Release here

Play the following example, using only the third finger. Apply the DAMPER PEDAL as indicated. LISTEN to the result!

Note how pleasant the sustained effect is to the ears!—because *all of the notes are related* and form a chord.

W. M. Co. 5770

Now play the next example,
fingering and pedalling as indicated. (B)

This time the effect is blurred and very unpleasant because the notes are *not* related and form a series of dissonances annoying to the ear.

Play also the following examples. (C) (D)

It is evident to the ear that Example C is pleasant because only chords *of the same harmony* are sustained together.

Example D binds together, by use of the pedal, chords that are different harmonies and the effect is a tonal jangle of harsh sounds.

It is quite obvious therefore, that great care must be used in applying the pedal. One's playing can be enriched or marred by its use. Fortunately, at this stage of advancement, it is simply necessary to follow the pedal markings strictly as indicated and correct results will follow.

THE SYNCOPATED PEDAL

The pedal should be applied, *not* at the moment the keys are being pressed down, but *immediately afterward*. The reason for this will become clear after the pupil has advanced further along the road to pianism. For the present it is sufficient that he forms the habit of pedalling after the keys have been struck. This is sometimes called "syncopated pedalling." The following exercises will be found helpful.

EXAMPLE 1

Count *"ONE and TWO and THREE and FOUR and"* etc.
Pedal *down* on "and"—*up* on the numerals (1, 2, 3, 4)

EXAMPLE 2

Count "ONE, TWO, THREE, etc.
Pedal *down* immediately *after* "ONE" in each bar.
Release pedal as you *say* "ONE" in each bar.

Teacher's Note: It is advisable to have pupils practise *left hand alone with pedal* in all examples employing pedal until its use becomes automatic and instinctive. This is particularly helpful because in the earlier grades the pedal is used mostly for the purpose of sustaining basses. Only the most elementary pedal effects should be attempted during the study of this book.

Distant Bells

14

practise pedal with C major scale (1 finger) and then LH only of this piece.

L. Streabbog

Andante

Hand stg.

with pedal & dynamics

To develop technical fluency — use John Thompson's "First Studies in Style."

W. M. Co. 5770

THE PEDAL WITH ARPEGGIO GROUPS

Use the pedal exactly as marked in the following example.

The arpeggio groups should be rolled rather than fingered and *tossed* from one hand to the other.

Follow the marks of expression and try to make a colourful sketch of this exercise from Duvernoy.

Etude

J. B. Duvernoy

TEACHER'S NOTE: This short college song is presented purely as a recreation, and is not an *essential* part of the MODERN METHOD FOR THE PIANO. From the pedagogic stand-point, its study will promote better left hand control, since the LEFT HAND is required to play both *melody and accompaniment*. Incidently it offers an example for a pedal exercise.

Bill Grogan's Goat
(Humoresque for Left Hand alone)

College Song

In the following piece the CHORDS should sound as though they were played on a church organ. This means that each chord must be as sustained as possible, that is, one chord must be connected to the next by means of the PEDAL.

NOTE THE NEW PEDAL MARK!

This sign is used to show that the PEDAL is released and pressed down again *immediately* in order to preserve an unbroken legato. thus——

Sometimes you will see a pedal mark like this——

Or the word Ped. may be used like this——

Always remember that all three markings have the **same meaning**.

In Church

Andante, sostenuto e semplice

Hands sep, + Then together.

accented practice —

CARL CZERNY (*pronounced Chair'ne*) was born in Vienna, Feb. 21, 1791. His father, who was a music teacher, taught him to play the piano, and later, he received instruction from Beethoven. At the age of twenty-five, a European concert tour was planned for him but there were so many disturbances because of war in Europe, that the public appearance was abandoned. He, therefore, decided to devote all of his time to teaching. His success was remarkable and among many noted artists to receive their training from him was the celebrated Franz Liszt, the greatest pianist that ever lived. As a composer, Czerny published over one thousand works of which his many studies for the piano have been used steadily year after year.

Be careful to observe slurring the chord progressions.
Play the passages in semiquavers with clean finger legato.

A Frolic in Velocity

C. Czerny (adapted)

For further development of finger legato — use John Thompson's "The Hanon Studies".

W. M. Co. 5770

THE minstrel show was definitely an American form of entertainment. Minstrel companies were made up of a cast of men who blacked their faces, dressed in gaudy costumes, sang negro songs, played banjos, danced taps, clogs, etc. Dan Emmett, the composer of *Dixie* was a member of the *Virginia Minstrels*. Stephen Foster wrote *Old Folks at Home* and other of his famous songs for *Christy's Minstrels*. About 1870, when minstrelsy was exceedingly popular, a coloured composer, James A. Bland, wrote this beautiful plantation melody which has been sung by the greatest artists in concert and over the radio.

Carry Me Back to Old Virginny

James A. Bland

Introduction
Moderato

Thumb UNDER the 3rd Finger

Hand in NORMAL five-finger position

Hand position with thumb UNDER the third finger

Right Hand Exercise

Reverie

Andantino

NOTE: See page 89 for supplementary exercises. Thoroughness in smooth passage playing is necessary.

3rd Finger CROSSING THUMB

Hand in NORMAL five-finger position

Hand position with third finger OVER thumb

Left Hand Exercise

Puck

Allegretto

mf scherzando

pp

pp

W. M. Co. 5770

Frédéric François Chopin was born in a village six miles from Warsaw, Poland. His father, a Frenchman who had come from Nancy, was a captain in the National Guard. He conducted a private school for the sons of the Polish nobility where Frédéric received his early education. His mother, for whom he entertained profound love, was pure Polish. She encouraged him at an early age to study music and he advanced so rapidly that, at the age of nine years, he played a concerto at a public concert. After the concert he seems to have been more concerned about his new collar than the effect his brilliant playing made on the audience for he remarked to his mother: "Everybody was looking at my collar."

In 1831, Chopin went to Paris to make his home. It was there, in the drawing-rooms of the French aristocracy, that he fascinated his hearers with that wonderful playing which earned for him the name, *The Poet of the Piano*. He was never of robust health and during the last years of his life his frail body broke under the strain of his concerts, teaching and social activities. He died in Paris at the age of 39.

Prélude in A Major

Chopin (1810-1849)

SCALES IN EXTENDED FORM

Thorough familiarity with scales means better keyboard technique

SCALES should now be practised in extended form— that is, NOT DIVIDED BETWEEN THE HANDS. Continue with the preparatory exercise on page 89 until the hands can be passed over smoothly.

Rules and Guides for the fingering of all the scales are shown on the the charts, page 86. New scales should be studied at the direction of the teacher.

When the scale in extended form has been mastered, each hand separately, it is advisable to practise the hands together *first in contrary motion,* since this causes the *same fingers* to be used simultaneously in both hands. Later, they may be studied in parallel motion.

THE C MAJOR SCALE IN CONTRARY MOTION

THE C MAJOR SCALE IN PARALLEL MOTION

VARIATIONS on a theme frequently enhance the beauty of the original air. It is claimed that the Elizabethan Virginal and lute players established the first steps. Beginning with Haydn and Mozart and developed by Beethoven, the composers Schubert, Schumann, and Brahms, all have written examples which students of music will enjoy as they progress in piano playing. This little old time waltz, written many years ago by an American composer of teaching pieces exemplifies the popularity of variations of that period.

Starlight Waltz

C. S. Brainard

Set a good tempo and keep it intact.

A waltz in $\frac{3}{8}$ time is played considerably faster than one in $\frac{3}{4}$.

Note the accent on the second beat which occurs very frequently.

The last Variation may require separate practise for the right hand. The groups of semiquavers should be cleanly fingered and rolled off at the end of each phrased group.

Pedal only where marked.

W. M. Co. 5770

TEACHING THE MINOR SCALES

There are two distinct approaches to teaching the MINOR SCALES; (1) the RELATIVE minor; (2) the PARALLEL minor. Although each method has decided merit, teachers differ in the choice of approach. For that reason both methods have been presented in the following pages and either may be used according to preference.

WHY DIFFERENT METHODS ARE USED

Teachers who use the RELATIVE minor approach do so because the *key signature remains the same* for both major and minor.

The PARALLEL minor approach is used because it causes less complication in the matter of fingering—especially in the WHITE KEY MINORS, where the *fingering remains exactly the same* as in the PARALLEL MAJORS. However, the pupil should *finally* know BOTH approaches. For instance, after having played G major, he should be able at once to play either G minor or E minor with equal facility. A debate, therefore, on the merits of either approach is rather useless.

HARMONIC MINOR FIRST

In the opinion of the author it seems unwise to attempt teaching all three forms of the minor (to the average pupil) at once. An old rule: "One thing at a time," is quite applicable to minor scales Experience proves that if the Harmonic form is learned first *in all keys*, the result is one of less confusion and more perfect mastery, both analytical and technical, on the part of the pupil. Afterwards, when the scales are being reviewed for the second time, the other forms of the minor may be taught, thus showing the *evolution* of the minor scale from NATURAL to MELODIC to HARMONIC.

See chart on pages 86 and 87.

Every major scale has a *Relative Minor* scale.

The Relative Minor scale begins on the sixth degree of the Major scale.

There are three forms of the minor scale, namely NATURAL minor, MELODIC minor and HARMONIC minor. For the present we shall consider only the HARMONIC minor.

The Harmonic Minor is formed from the (Relative) Major Scale by *raising the Seventh note* (of the minor scale) *one semitone*

A MINOR is *relative* to C MAJOR.

The fingering for A minor is the same as that for A major.

Observe that the minor scale employs the same notes as the (Relative) major scale – *except the seventh*, which is raised ONE SEMITONE

A minor key has the *same signature* as the Relative Major Key.

NOTE TO TEACHERS: Teachers who prefer to teach all three forms of the minor scale at this point should use the chart on pages 86 and 87.

The Parallel Minor Approach

Every major scale has a *Parallel Minor* scale.

The Parallel Minor scale begins on the *same note* as the Major scale.

There are three forms of the minor scale, namely NATURAL minor, MELODIC minor and HARMONIC minor. For the present we shall consider only the HARMONIC minor.

The Harmonic Minor is formed from the (Parallel) Major Scale by *lowering the Third and Sixth degrees one semitone*

C minor is *parallel* to C major.

The fingering remains the same as in the major scale.

Observe that the lowered notes always occur at the point where the *third fingers play to - gether.* (This rule will hold good for the first five WHITE KEY minor scales, i.e. C, G, D, A, E.)

MAJOR and MINOR MODES

Note that the First Theme of this piece is in the key of C major and that the Second Theme is in the key of A minor, relative to C major. This is but another illustration of the *Law of Contrast* — the first law of all Art.

A Journey in the Arctic

First Theme
Allegretto

Second Theme
Melodic minor scale

Suggestions for Supplementary Material — *use John Thompson's "First Studies in Style."*

W. M. Co. 5770

4th Finger CROSSING THUMB

No. 2. For the Left Hand

PREPARATORY EXERCISES

No. 1. For the Right Hand

The Sky Pilot

Moderato

Hide and Seek

Allegro moderato

See page 87 for origin of melodic minor scale.

W. M. Co. 5770

A Study in smooth FINGER LEGATO

Old French Melody

IT is frequently claimed that the national music of Hungary is really the music of the Hungarian gypsies. At any rate, the Hungarian composer, Franz Liszt, wove the gypsy music of native folk-tunes into fifteen Hungarian Rhapsodies. This type of music is characterized by abrupt changes in mood and rhythm and, therefore, has tonal effects all its own. In the following example, be sure to play with marked contrast, the opening theme, which should be played in a slow tempo and melancholy mood, and the fiery second theme; a theme which should be alive with animation and dash.

The Gypsy Camp

Very slowly (sad and melancholy)

Suggestions for Supplementary Material— use John Thompson's "The Hanon Studies."

W. M. Co. 5770

Very fast (with fire and dash)

Presto

GRAND OPERA is a play set to music in which the characters act and sing their thoughts instead of speaking them. "Don Giovanni" (*Don Juan*) was written by the great Austrian composer, Wolfgang Amadeus Mozart. The story by Lorenzo da Ponte is based on a version called *The Stone Guest.* This great opera was produced for the first time in Prague in 1787. There are two acts and the plot is laid in Seville during the Seventeenth Century.

Don Juan, a gay Spanish nobleman, and his mischievous servant, Leporello, are always making people unhappy. Don tries to press his attentions on Anna, the beautiful daughter of the Commandant, who unexpectedly arrives. They fight a duel; the Commandant is killed while Don Juan and his servant escape. The townspeople erect a statue in honour of their dead commandant. While fleeing along a deserted road, Don Juan meets an old sweetheart, Elvira, who reproaches him but he escapes, leaving her alone with Leporello. We now find the gay cavalier in his palace flattering a beautiful peasant girl, Zerlina. He orders a gala festival and we hear the strains of the "MINUET", that graceful and courtly dance of the incomparable Mozart. Don Juan attempts to run away with Zerlina but is prevented by the appearance of Anna in search of the murderer of her father and Elvira who seeks revenge; Don Juan again takes to his heels. That night, near the statue of the slain commandant, Don and his servant plan other schemes. Suddenly, the statue speaks, warning them to mend their ways. Flippantly, Don invites the statue to dine with them. During the banquet, a heavy tramping is heard on the stairs. The statue enters the room, Don Juan seizes the marble hand when instantly the floor opens and demons drag the wicked Don Juan down amid flames and lightning.

Minuet from "Don Juan"

Mozart (1756-1791)

The MAZURKA is a lively round dance and one of the national dances of Poland. Remember, that in all dance forms, rhythm is of paramount importance. Keep a steady, even tempo and observe all ACCENTS.

This piece is in the key of A MINOR— relative minor to C major.

A Little Polish Dance
Mazurka

ETUDE

Allegro   Adapted from Köhler

The Hare and the Hounds

Additional scale exercises will be found on page 90

Try to play "Off We Go" as gracefully as possible.
Preserve an even finger legato and toss off the end of each phrase, indicated by the curved line.

Preparatory Exercise

The following exercise should be practised daily until the chords lie comfortably under the fingers and until the change can be made without effort.

Off We Go!

Allegro grazioso

L. Streabbog

Up-arm stroke and arm impulse

This tune is quite characteristic of the gypsy life in the old days of Russia. It has all of the rhythmic features and the spirit of the furious dances so typical of the Russian peasants.

It should be played with a free, fiery abandon employing sharp accents and sharp staccato. The accented chords, coming as they do at the end of a short phrase, should be played with decided UP-ARM strokes. Be sure to play the repeated chords that follow with *one-arm impulse*. Use pedal sparingly.

Two Preparatory Exercises

No. 1. For the Right Hand

No. 2. For the Left Hand

Dark Eyes

Russian Gypsy Dance

Folk Song

W. M. Co. 5770

CADENCE CHORDS

What a *period* (full stop) is to a sentence, a *cadence* is to music. In other words, a *CADENCE* is the *end of a musical sentence*.

The principal TRIADS of the scale are those found on the FIRST, FOURTH and FIFTH degrees. They are important because they are *the chords used in forming CADENCES*.

These chords are named TONIC, SUB-DOMINANT and DOMINANT as shown below.

Familiar Cadences

Here is a study in CHORD ANALYSIS.

Write the *name* and *inversion* of each chord in the following example. When you can play the Preparatory Exercise, follow with the Etude showing the chords in broken form.

Preparatory Exercise

Write name of each chord ....

Étude

For further development of the rolling attack— use John Thompson's "The Hanon Studies".

The Chord of the DOMINANT-SEVENTH

You have learned that TRIADS on the **1st**, **4th** and **5th** degrees of the scale, TONIC, SUB-DOMINANT and DOMINANT are called CADENCE CHORDS.

The TRIAD on the 5th degree, the DOMINANT, often appears with the addition of a minor 7th—(1,3,5,7) and is known as the CHORD OF THE DOMINANT SEVENTH.

Chord of the Dominant-Seventh

The minor seventh is a pleasing dissonance and adds a feeling of *motion* to the chord, since all dissonances are active in character and must move to a consonant interval before a feeling of rest is secured.

BECAUSE THE CHORD CONTAINS FOUR NOTES, THREE INVERSIONS ARE POSSIBLE

Dominant 7th Chord and THREE INVERSIONS

Root position   First Inversion   Second Inversion   Third Inversion

CADENCE CHORDS USING THE DOMINANT-SEVENTH CHORD

Play the following Cadences and note the feeling of activity given the Dominant chord by reason of the added minor seventh.

THE DOMINANT-SEVENTH IN ARPEGGIO FORM

Examine the pieces studied thus far in this book and see how many *Dominant-Seventh Chords* you can locate.

50

Ludwig van Beethoven, one of the greatest of musicians was born Dec. 17, 1770, in Bonn-on-the-Rhine, Germany. His father, a tenor singer in the village choir, was very cruel and used to beat the boy sometimes when he did not practise. His mother was kind and patient. Her death, when he was seventeen years old, brought him sorrow which he never seemed to forget. When still a boy, he was made assistant organist in the cathedral, a position which he held until 1792. He also played second viola in the theatre orchestra. One day when he was on a visit to Vienna, he met Mozart who was so impressed with Beethoven's playing that he exclaimed: "He will give the world something worth listening to."

Beethoven loved to wander through the cool forest, listen to the voices of nature and compose his music in such surroundings. At the age of thirty, he began to grow deaf and in later years, he was unable to hear his own compositions.

Romanze

from 5th Sonatina

Beethoven (1770-1827)

A Grace Note is a little note used as an ornament. It has no time value and should be "flicked" into the principal note which follows as quickly as possible. It is always shown as a small note with a slanting line drawn through its stem, thus, ♪.

W. M. Co. 5770

ALLA BREVE

When the TIME SIGNATURE shows a line drawn through the broken circle thus, ¢, it is called *Alla Breve* time and it indicates *two counts to the bar* with *one count to each minim.*

Learn the following example first in four-four TIME, i. e., four counts to the bar and one count to each crotchet. When it has been perfectly mastered, increase the *tempo* counting but *two to the bar* and *one to each minim.*

Scherzino

See glossary on page 88 for the meaning of *Scherzino.*

W. M. Co. 5770

Liszt at the age of 14
Courtesy "The Musical Quarterly"

Franz Liszt, born in Raiding, Hungary, was a very delicate and sickly boy until he reached the age of six. Then, one day, while his father was playing a *Concerto* on the piano, little Franz came up beside him and implored him to repeat the last movement over and over again. "What would you like to be when you grow up?" asked his father, lighting his pipe. "That man there!" said the boy pointing to a picture of Beethoven. The next day his father began to give him lessons. Franz spent hours practising the scales and made such rapid progress that he played in a concert by the time he was nine years old. The performance was so brilliant that everybody wanted to meet him and six of the nobles present raised funds to send him to Vienna for study with Czerny. Later "little Liszt" enjoyed a greater triumph for, when Beethoven heard him play, he was so amazed by Franz's wonderful technique that he went to the stage, grasped the child, and kissed him on the forehead.

Because the little village of Raiding was rather isolated, it became a camping place for wandering gypsies, who, as they arrived in their wagons, would pitch their tents in the square. At night, amid the blaze of great bonfires, the men with violins and cymbals, and the girls in brilliant coloured dresses, ear-rings, and necklaces, would dance and sing the rugged folk-tunes of Romany. Little Franz would drink in these weirdly abrupt rhythms and melodies which later became so evident in his famous *Hungarian Rhapsodies*.

Theme from Liebesträume No. 3
A Dream of Love

Liszt (1811-1886)

Here is an example of sudden and abrupt contrast in mood, typical of Slavonic music. Note that the first theme is played very slowly and in lyric style— which is to say, in the manner of a song. It is rather pensive in character. But at the double bar it suddenly bursts into a very excitable dance, played *Allegro*. The dancers whirl about gathering more and more impetus until the bar marked *molto rit.*— (much ritard) is reached. Here in one bar the tempo slows down to that of the opening theme and the piece ends on the lament with which it began.

Preparatory Exercises

A Little Slavonic Rhapsody

Andante

Allegro con brio

W. M. Co. 5770

Tempo I°

ORATORIO derives its name from the oratory (*a chapel in a church*) in which a monk, Fillipo Neri, used to deliver his sermons on Biblical history during the Sixteenth Century. These discourses were illustrated by sacred songs. The modern oratorio consists of solos, duets, broad majestic choruses and recitatives with full orchestral accompaniment. It is distinguished from opera by the absence of action, costumes, and scenery. Usually the story is based on some text from the Bible. In the Eighteenth Century, Bach, Handel and Haydn developed the oratorio to its highest standard.

The Messiah was written by George Frideric Handel, a German composer, who spent many years in England and who lies buried in Westminster Abbey. The story concerns the prophecies and coming of Jesus. It is said that Handel wrote this long oratorio in twenty-four days. When a great choir sang the *Hallelujah Chorus* at a performance of the *Messiah* in London, King George II and his nobles, rose to their feet to show their reverence for this great music. The entire audience stood up with him and to this very day, it is customary for an audience to stand during the singing of this chorus.

Oratorio at the Bach Festival

Hallelujah Chorus

Handel (1685-1759)

Allegro

Etude

Roll the left hand groups.

Skipping Through The Forest

Vivace

Suggestions for Supplementary Material— use John Thompson's "First Studies in Style."

W. M. Co. 5770

ARPEGGIOS
(Broken Chords)

A broken chord is called an *Arpeggio*.

Arpeggio is an Italian word meaning "in the style of a harp."

Arpeggios exist in many forms but small hands should be restricted to arpeggios in closed form— that is, chords that remain in the octave position— until sufficient stretch has been developed to encompass the crossing called for in extended arpeggios, smoothly and easily.

The following forms will be found very beneficial as well as affording interesting practice.

RULE FOR FINGERING: 1st, 2nd and 5th fingers always used by both hands in all positions. The use of the 3rd or 4th finger is governed by the stretch involved. If there is *only one white key* between the note played by the 5th finger and the next note of the chord, *use the fourth finger.* When there are *two white keys* lying between, *use the third finger.*

Practise with well articulated finger legato.

This form should be practised with the Rolling Attack and sharply tossed off.

Practise in various keys as directed by the Teacher.

Étude

H. Berens

Étude

Carl Czerny

Hinkey, Dinkey, "Parley Voo"

Arpeggio Variations

The doughboy he went over the top
Because he had no place to stop,
From gay Paree he heard guns roar
And all he learned was "je t'adore."

World War Song

Con anima

Preparatory Exercise

Deep River

The songs handed down to our generation which were sung by the negro slaves on the plantations at "pray'r meetin's", baptisms, and on the levees, often referred to as *Spirituals*, are traditional of American life. The music is full of rare and sorrowful melody, rich, colourful and warm as any folk-tune. The Bohemian composer, Dvořák, used some of these tunes in his symphony, *From the New World*.

Plantation Hymn

Moths
Scherzino

TRIPLET is the name given to a group of *THREE* notes that are intended to be played in the time ordinarily given to *TWO* notes of equal value.

For instance:— THREE quavers played in the time of TWO quavers,

or

THREE crotchets played in the time of TWO crotchets and so on.

In the following example there are triplets applied to scale figures.

Play this example with clean, articulated finger legato. It is fine practice for developing evenness of touch.

Grandpapa Jonathan
Diatonic figures in Triplets

For additional exercises in articulated finger legato — use John Thompson's "The Hanon Studies".

W. M. Co. 5770

Georges Bizet was born in Paris, October 25, 1838. His mother taught him the rudiments of music when he was only four years of age and he was sent to the Conservatory before he was nine. He won the Grand Prix de Rome when he was nineteen and while studying in Italy he submitted, instead of the prescribed Mass, an Opera which was highly praised. He was a remarkably fine pianist although he did not perform in public. His fame and renown rest upon his two *L'Arlésienne Suites* and the opera, *Carmen*, which placed him in the front rank of modern French composers. The example following is from the first act of *Carmen* and shows the scene wherein Carmen sings and dances in her attempt to captivate Don José, a Spanish captain of the guard. A *Habanera* is a Spanish song and dance which really dates back to Africa by way of Cuba. It was first imported into Cuba by negro slaves after which it naturally found its way into Spain. As in all dance forms *rhythm is uppermost*. Note the alla breve TIME— which means two counts to the bar and one count to each minim. Learn it first, however, in four-four time. Let the staccato be sharp and brittle and do not overlook the two-note slur in each bar.

Habanera from "Carmen"

Bizet (1838-1875)

The Bee and the Clover

Adam Geibel

Allegro giocoso

W. M. Co. 5770

Broken Chords in Triplets

A Trial Flight

The TRILL is an ornamental figure which is very effective when well performed. It consists of an alternating shake between the principal note (the note written) and the next note above. The early keyboard instruments had very little sustaining qualities and the Trill was used originally to give the effect of a long, sustained tone. The number of notes played in a Trill is entirely optional with the performer.

This is the sign of the Trill,

TRILL STUDY

Play the trill figures in the following example with close finger action. The fingers should actually "ride" the keys.

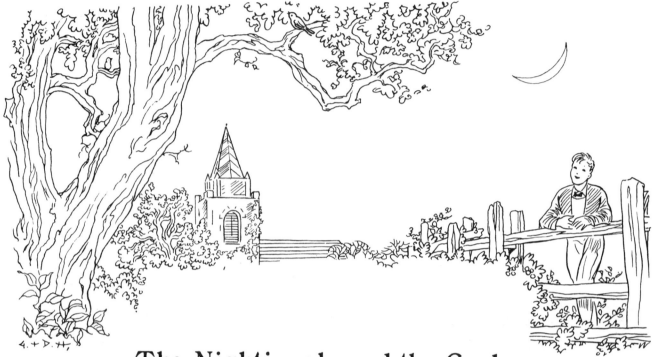

The Nightingale and the Cuckoo

Allegro

Two Guitars
Russian Gypsy Song

Slowly

PREPARATORY EXERCISE

Learn to trill first in semiquavers like this.

Later in semiquavers like this.

No. 1   etc.

No. 2

The waved line (∿) after *tr* indicates the duration of the TRILL.

Song of the Birds

Moderato

Jacques **Offenbach** was born in Cologne, Germany but at an early age settled in Paris and became a naturalized Frenchman. At the age of fourteen, he joined the orchestra of the Opera Comique as a cellist. He originated a rather individual style of comic opera known as *opéra bouffe* many of which, together with his ballet pantomime, were produced in his own theatre, the Bouffes-Parisiens. His greatest work, the *Tales of Hoffmann,* was produced after his death. The first performance was given in Paris, Feb. 10, 1881.

The poet Hoffmann and his student friends of Nuremburg, are making merry in the tavern while he tells of his three unhappy love adventures. The scene changes, Hoffmann is given a pair of magic glasses through which he sees Olympia, his first love, who is in reality a beautiful mechanical doll. He pleads to dance with her and they waltz so madly and rapidly that Hoffmann falls in a swoon. The glasses break and he learns that his love was an illusion. In the next act (in Venice), he discovers his friend, Niklaus, with a captivating lady, Giulietta, seated in a gondola, singing the "Barcarolle" in the mystic moonlight. He falls in love with her, fights a duel with his rival, and kills him but, to the bitter disappointment of Hoffmann, Giulietta elopes with another. He then goes to Munich and wins the heart of the lovely Antonia, a delicate singer with a wonderful voice, whose doctor warns her that if she sings she will bring on a fatal illness. The wedding of Hoffmann and Antonia is set for the next day. In her happiness she sings and falls lifeless in her father's arms. The "Tales" are ended, the students depart and Hoffmann, sad and lonely, is consoled by the Muse of Poetry.

Olympia, the Dancing Doll — Act I

Barcarolle from Tales of Hoffmann

Play with a swinging six-eighth rhythm to suggest a swaying gondola drifting under moonlight, a night in Venice.

Offenbach (1819-1880)

80

Franz Joseph Haydn was born in Rohrau, Austria, in 1732. His genius attracted attention when he was very young and he is often called the father of instrumental music. In his early thirties, he enjoyed the patronage and friendship of the wealthy Prince Esterhazy and in consequence, spent much time in Hungary. While there, he developed a keen interest in the music of the Hungarian gypsies. The composition below is an air from the last movement of Haydn's trio for piano, violin and 'cello, very properly called the "Gypsy Rondo". This music is characteristic of the Gypsy folk, full of light-heartedness and the joy of living. All of Haydn's work is characterized by simplicity, perfect finish, the avoidance of meaningless phrases, and firmness of design. Use clearly articulated finger legato in the right hand in playing the "Gypsy Rondo" and do not overlook the occasional staccato notes.

Haydn in 1762
(From a painting by Longhi)
Courtesy Brooklyn Museum

Theme from Gypsy Rondo

Haydn (1732–1809)

W. M. Co. 5770

In the following examples, the groups in semiquavers should be rolled rather than fingered. Keep the fingers close to the keys and roll the groups inward and upward, tossing off sharply on the last note. This gives a "sparkle" not obtainable with the usual finger legato.

Preparatory Exercise

March of the Gnomes

Allegretto

RECITAL PIECE

From

Will o' the Wisp

Vivo

Albert Jungmann

Jocularity

Scale Fingering Chart

SCALES BEGINNING ON WHITE KEYS

Right Hand

The Thumb falls on the FIRST and FOURTH notes of the scale.

Left-Hand

The Thumb falls on the FIRST and FIFTH notes of the scale.

FINGER GUIDE
THIRD FINGERS OF BOTH HANDS **ALWAYS** PLAY TOGETHER.

There are two exceptions to the above rules— the scales of B major and F major. They are fingered as follows:

B MAJOR—*Begin with FOURTH finger in the left hand.*

F MAJOR—*End with FOURTH finger in the right hand.*

FINGER GUIDE
(for exceptional scales)
THUMBS OF BOTH HANDS **ALWAYS** PLAY TOGETHER.

MINOR SCALES

The WHITE KEY MINOR Scales are fingered exactly the same as the WHITE KEY MAJOR Scales.

SCALES BEGINNING ON **BLACK** KEYS

MAJOR SCALES

Right Hand

Fourth finger on B♭ (or A♯).

Left Hand

Fourth finger on the 4th note of the scale. Begin with THIRD finger.

There is one exception to the above rules— the major scale on G♭ (or F♯). For this scale use the rule of TWO'S and THREE'S, i.e., where TWO **BLACK** KEYS lie together, use the fingers 2 and 3. Where THREE **BLACK** KEYS lie together use the fingers 2, 3 and 4.

MINOR SCALES

B♭ MINOR }
E♭ MINOR } *TWO'S and THREE'S in BOTH hands.*

A♭ (or G♯) MINOR—*Fingered same as MAJOR.*

D♭ (C♯) MINOR }

Right Hand
FOURTH finger on the 2nd note of scale.

G♭ (F♯) MINOR }

Left Hand
TWO'S and THREE'S.

W. M. Co. 5770

The Three Minor Forms

SHOWING THE EVOLUTION OF THE MINOR SCALE

C MAJOR SCALE

6th degree

NATURAL MINOR FORM: This is the oldest form of the MINOR SCALE. Beginning on the **6th degree** it ascended and descended on exactly the same notes contained in the RELATIVE MAJOR SCALE.

6th and 7th raised. Descends same as the Natural form

A MINOR SCALE RELATIVE TO C MAJOR SCALE

MELODIC MINOR FORM: This form appeared at a later period. It was felt that in order to establish the "feel" of the tonality in A MINOR a leading note (raised 7th) was necessary. However, the skip of a tone and-a-half (from the 6th to the raised 7th) was unpleasant to ears not accustomed to such jumps. To obviate this, the 6th was also raised one semitone. Since a leading note is not necessary in descending, the MELODIC MINOR scale descends on the same notes as those that make up the RELATIVE MAJOR Scale.

7th degree raised

HARMONIC MINOR FORM: This form is most frequently used in present day music. The 7th degree is raised one semitone, both in ascending and descending.

GLOSSARY

of

Terms, Abbreviations and Signs used in

John Thompson's

SECOND GRADE BOOK

Abbreviation	TERMS	Signs	Abbreviation	TERMS	Signs
	Accent: Emphasize or stress.....	> ∧		**Mezzo Forte:** Moderately loud.	*mf*
	Alla Breve: Two beats to the bar —one beat to each minim........	¢		**Mezzo Piano:** Moderately soft.	*mp*
allarg.	**Allargando:** A slackening of the tempo......................			**Moderato:** Moderately.	
	Allegretto: Gay and moderately lively.			**Molto:** Much.	
	Allegro: Quick and cheerful.			**Non Troppo:** Not too much.	
	Andante: Moderately slow.			**Pause:** To hold or prolong beyond the allotted time...............	⌢
	Andantino: A little faster than Andante.			**Piano:** Softly.................	*p*
	Animato: Animated.			**Pianissimo:** Very softly.......	*pp*
	A Tempo: Resume original speed.			**Poco:** Little.	
	Cadence: The end of a musical sentence.			**Poco a Poco:** Little by little.	
	Chromatic: Proceeding by semi-tones.			**Presto:** Quick, nimble, rapid.	
	Con Anima: With animation.			**Reverie:** A dreamy composition.	
	Con Brio: With brilliance.		*rit.*	**Ritardando:** A gradual slowing of the time.	
	Con Moto: With motion.			**Romanza:** Romance.	
cresc.	**Crescendo:** A gradual increasing in tone. Shown also with the sign.	<	*scherz.*	**Scherzando:** Playfully, gaily.	
				Scherzino: A short composition in playful or whimsical style.	
D.C. al Fine	**Da Capo Al Fine:** Return to the beginning of the piece and play to the end of the bar marked *Fine*.			**Semplice:** Simply.	
				Sempre: Always.	
Dim.	**Diminuendo:** A gradual decreasing in tone. Shown also........	>	*sfz*	**Sforzando:** Forcing: the sudden accenting of a note or chord.....	
	Dolce: Sweetly.		*ten.*	**Sostenuto:** Sustained. Indicated by a line over a note or chord....	
Dom.	**Dominant:** The 5th degree of the scale.	V	*stacc.*	**Staccato:** Detached...........	
	e: And			**Staccatissimo:** Very short and detached......................	
	Espressivo: With expression.		*Sub. Dom.*	**Sub-Dominant:** The 4th degree of the scale.	IV
	Forte: Loud: Strong.	*f*		**Syncopation:** Caused when accents fall upon weak beats, meanwhile suppressing the natural accented beats.	
	Fortissimo: Very loud: very strong......................	*ff*			
	Giocoso: Sportively.			**Tempo:** Time.	
	Grace Notes: Little notes added as ornaments to give a graceful effect. They have no time value and should be played as quickly as possible...................	♪		**Tempo I:** Resume original Time.	
				Tonic: The 1st degree, or keynote of the scale.	I
	Grazioso: Gracefully: smoothly.			**Trill:** A bird-like effect produced by rapidly alternating two adjoining notes of the scale...........	*tr*⌣
	Leger Lines: Added lines above or below the staff.			**Triplets:** Three notes of equal value played in the time of two notes of the same value.	3
	Legato: Smooth and connected.				
legg.	**Leggiero:** Light, easy, nimble.			**Vivace:** Lively, vivacious, light, gay.	

W. M. Co. 5770

TECHNICAL DRILLS

Additional exercises to be assigned at the option of the teacher during the study of this book. Each has a specific purpose.

Trill for 1-2 and 4-5

Trill for 3-2 and 3-4

Combined Trill Figures

Passing the Thumb under the Second finger
Follow the fingering exactly

Passing the Thumb under the Third finger

Passing the Thumb under the Fourth finger

The Chromatic Scale

Passing the Hand over in Arpeggio Figures

Wrist Staccato (Sixths)

W. M. Co. 5770

Printed in Great Britain by Hobbs the Printers of Southampton 3/92

Certificate of Merit

This certifies that

. . . .

has successfully completed

"JOHN THOMPSON'S SECOND GRADE BOOK"

and is eligible for promotion to

"JOHN THOMPSON'S THIRD GRADE BOOK"

. . . .
Teacher

Date. . . . .